THREE-MINUTE SKITS AND SONGS

Compiled by Rebecca Daniel

illustrated by
Corbin Hillam

Cover by Janet Skiles

Shining Star Publications, Copyright © 1991
A Division of Good Apple

ISBN No. 0-86653-628-0

Standardized Subject Code TA ac

Printing No. 9

Shining Star
A Division of Frank Schaffer Publications, Inc.
23740 Hawthorne Boulevard, Torrance, CA 90505-5927

Unless otherwise indicated, the New International Version of the Bible was used in preparing the activities in this book.

TABLE OF CONTENTS

TO THE TEACHER/PARENT

Three-Minute Bible Skits and Songs is a book of quick skits and songs that can be presented in the classroom, in the church worship service, or any other setting where short skits would be appropriate. Have you been searching for a unique way to present famous Bible stories to your class? Most children love to perform, so why not consider using a skit or song? The reproducible skits and songs make it quick and easy. There are endless numbers of ways to present these materials. Here are just a few:

1. The Bible-based skits and singable songs may be incorporated into a string of performances to be presented by different children.
2. In a classroom setting, the skits can be used to introduce or reinforce the study of a particular Bible story.
3. The skits can be practiced, memorized and presented to a congregation when only a short period of time is available.
4. Children can break into small groups, and each group can practice and present the same skit to the other groups.
5. Skits and songs can be tape-recorded and presented as radio programs. Later the tapes can be sent to friends and family who live far away.
6. The skits and songs make wonderful puppet plays.

The reproducible skit scripts and musical scores, a special costuming unit, and tips for directing and producing will make any performance hassle-free. No matter which skit or song you choose to perform, the children are sure to please the audience and have them standing in ovation with these Bible-based materials written especially for young Bible students.

Shining Star Publications, Copyright © 1991, A division of Good Apple

SS1885

PRODUCTION TIPS

If you are planning to present the three-minute skits and songs to a large audience, the following instructions may be helpful:

1. Begin by reading many skits to the children to find out which one they enjoy the most. Let the youngsters help decide which skit they will perform.

2. Once you have selected the skit you will perform, the Scripture account of the drama should be studied by all prospective cast members. After casting is completed, review the Scripture account before rehearsals begin.

3. Reread the skit with the children, making sure they understand the meanings of all words and have some idea of the background of the characters.

4. Selecting the cast can be accomplished by having various children read or repeat lines from the script. Listen to their interpretations of certain characters before selecting the cast.

5. When parts have been selected, make sure the young people emphasize how each participant in the story felt about what was happening. This will help them develop particular moods and feelings in their presentations.

6. Children should memorize their parts before rehearsal. Practice the speaking parts in small groups offstage several times before actually going to the stage to practice.

7. Do not tire the children by repeating the skit many times in one day. Shorter rehearsals over a longer period of time produce better results. We want dramatization to be a joy, not a task.

8. If costumes are to be used, a dress rehearsal the day before the final performance will help insure a smooth presentation.

OLD TESTAMENT SKITS

GOD MADE THE WORLD

Based on Genesis 1, 2
by Helen Kitchell Evans

CAST OF CHARACTERS

Narrator
Five children

Narrator:	In the beginning, God made the earth and the skies. Then He gathered all the water together to make the oceans and seas. Then God said,
Child 1:	Let plants and trees grow on the earth.
Narrator:	Then God made the sun and the moon. He placed the stars in the sky. Then God said,
Child 2:	Let the waters be filled with fish.
Child 3:	Let the sky be filled with birds.
Child 4:	Let animals walk on the earth.
Narrator:	Then God made a man and a woman.
Child 5:	God did all this in six days.
Narrator:	God rested on the seventh day.

SS1885

IN THE GARDEN

Based on Genesis 3
by K. H. Munn

CAST OF CHARACTERS

Adam
Eve
Satan

Scene: Adam and Eve standing behind some sort of barrier where clothing cannot easily be seen (to give illusion of no clothing).

Adam: I'm glad God created us.

Eve: Yes, He is very good to us.

Adam: It's nice here. Great weather and all the good things we can eat.

Eve: Yes. Sure is nice. All those oranges, pineapples, grapes and other good things to eat.

Adam: Warm, too. I like that.

Eve: *(Points off into the distance.)* Only that one tree. God said never to eat the fruit. Sure nice that there are so many other good things here to eat.

(Satan walks up.)

Satan: Hi, folks. Nice here, isn't it? Getting all you want to eat? Tried everything?

(Note: The playlet ends here for audiences of over 15 years of age. For younger people, continue below.)

Adam: Yes. That reminds me, I'm hungry. Guess I'll go have a whole bunch of grapes. *(Walks offstage.)*

Satan: Are you hungry too, Eve? *(points)* That tree over there is the Tree of Good and Evil. If you eat fruit from it you will know good from evil, just like God.

Eve: That would be nice. I'll try it and Adam would probably like some, too.

Satan: Let's go get some. You'll like it.

SS1885

CAIN AND ABEL

Based on Genesis 4:1-16
by Marion Schoeberlein

CAST OF CHARACTERS

Abel   Voice of God
Cain   Narrator

Props: Big stick

Scene: A field where Abel has just made a sacrifice to God.

Narrator: Adam and Eve had two sons. One was called Cain and he was a farmer. The other one was named Abel and he was a shepherd.

There was a big difference between these two brothers. Cain was strong and sometimes cruel. He was very jealous of his brother because it always seemed that everyone liked Abel better.

This is the story of what happened to Cain after his jealousy got out of hand.

SS1885

Abel:	I have just sacrificed a lamb to the Lord, my brother.
Cain:	I can see you have. Don't you think I have eyes?
Abel:	I heard the voice of God, too, saying that He was pleased with my offering.
Cain:	Isn't that great? You always are pleasing everyone, little brother. You are the favorite at home with Father and Mother. You are the favorite with God. No one likes me and do you know why?
Abel:	I've never been able to understand it.
Cain:	It's because I'm strong and they're afraid of me. But someday God will see that I am the one worth being favored. Come to think of it, I will not wait until someday. I hate you, Abel, and I've always hated you!

(Cain picks up a big stick and begins attacking Abel.)

Abel:	Stop, Cain, stop, you are hurting me!
Cain:	I'm going to kill you. I want you out of the way. Then everyone, including God, will know I am the one to pay attention to.

(Cain hits Abel with the stick until he falls to the ground, dead.)

Voice of God:	*(from behind the curtain)* Where is Abel, your brother?
Cain:	Am I my brother's keeper?
Voice of God:	Cain, you killed your brother. Because you've done such an evil thing, I will make an outcast of you.

(Cain falls to the ground and puts his head in his hands.)

Cain:	Mercy, mercy, my God. If I am an outcast I will be killed by the wild beasts.
Voice of God:	Not so. I will put my mark on you and no one will kill you. Go now, to live in the land of Nod, east of Eden.

(Cain slowly rises and leaves the stage. His brother's body still lies at the other end of the stage.)

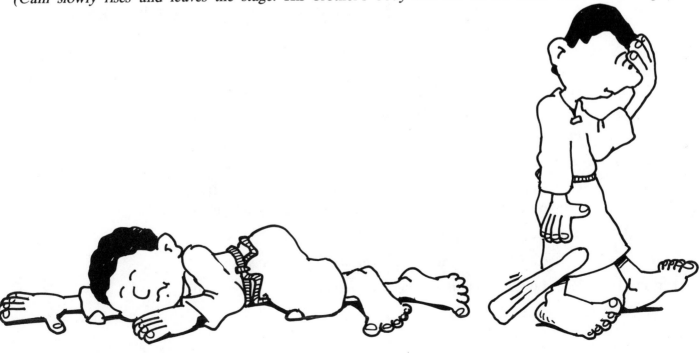

SS1885

THERE'S OLD NOAH

Based on Genesis 6, 7
by K. H. Munn

CAST OF CHARACTERS

Person #1
Person #2

Scene: Two people, gender inconsequential, standing. Person #1 points off into the distance.

Person #1: *(laughing)* Ha, ha. There's old Noah over there loading that great big ark with animals. He said God told him to. What a foolish man.

Person #2: Yes, he told me about it, too. The only people going onto the ark are his family and him. Noah says it's because God told him he's being saved because Noah has been obeying God. God told him a flood will kill everyone and every animal not on the ark.

Person #1: That's why he's taking all those animals along. Two of each kind. Supposed to be saving them from drowning, too. He has them all loaded now. What a foolish man.

(They put their arms around each other's shoulders.)

Person #1: God can't tell us what to do. I'm not afraid of Him. It's supposed to be because the people—that's us—have been so naughty. But being naughty is fun.

Person #2: Yes. Let's go be naughty. *(They walk off.)*

(After they have gone a few steps Person #1 puts his hand to his head.)

Person #1: Huh! I just felt a drop of water hit me on the head. Big one, too.

SS1885

ONTO THE ARK

Based on Genesis 7:9, 15, 16
by K. H. Munn

CAST OF CHARACTERS

Noah
Two bears
Two kittens

Scene: Two bears and two kittens are getting ready to load onto the ark. The kittens are in front of the bears.

Bear #1:   Get out of the way, you.

Kitten #1:   Why? Noah said for us to get on the ark. There is room for everyone and we were in line first.

Bear #1:   We're more important, that's why.

Kitten #1:   *(in disbelief)* Huh!

Bear #2:   We're big. That's what makes us important.

Kitten #2:   God says we are all important.

Bear #2:   Get out of the way. We're bigger!

(Noah walks up, looking concerned.)

Noah: What's going on here?

Bear #1:   We are important animals. These kittens should get out of our way.

Noah: God says all life is important. Besides, little children will need kittens to love someday. The kittens will go first.

    SS1885

GOD'S PROMISE

Based on Genesis 8-9:1-17
by K. H. Munn

CAST OF CHARACTERS

Ham
Shem
Noah

Scene: Ham and Shem standing on the deck of the ark. Ham looks off into the distance.

Ham: My! It's been raining a long time.

Shem: Yes. Dad sure took us for a long boat ride.

Ham: God told him to, you know.

Shem: Yes, He did. Good thing, too. It rained hard. It's finally drying up. I'm a pretty good swimmer but 150 days is a long time. Good thing God told Dad to put us into this ark.

Ham: Sure got old feeding all those animals, though.

Shem: Better than drowning. Nice that we're back down on the land, though. Look at those things eat! Those elephants eat plenty, too. I had to feed them. I know.

Ham: Wish we could know it was all over.

Shem: (Pointing.) Over there. Above the clouds. What's that? Sure pretty, isn't it? All those colors.

(Noah walks up smiling.)

Noah: Well, we're here, boys. (Points off to where Shem had pointed.) There's the rainbow. That's God's promise that He'll never send us another flood like this one. We're safe.

SS1885

SARAH LAUGHED AT GOD

Based on Genesis 18:1-15
by Marion Schoeberlein

CAST OF CHARACTERS

Abraham   Three Men (visitors)
Sarah   Narrator

Props: Bowl of food

Scene: Abraham and Sarah sit outside their tent for a few moments, then Sarah goes inside.

Narrator: Abraham and Sarah were old people. They had wanted a child for a long time, but God had not blessed them with one.

When God sent a messenger to Abraham announcing the birth of a son, Sarah laughed, because she was too old to have a child. This is the story of how anything is possible with God.

Abraham: Sarah, I see some men coming. I will go over to meet them. *(To three visitors.)* You look tired. Sit down and rest a while with me. I will bring you meat to eat and some bread.

(Three visitors nod and sit down.)

Abraham: *(Calling to his wife.)* Bring me bread and meat quickly, Sarah. Our visitors are hungry. *(A few minutes later Abraham goes into the tent and brings back a bowl of food and takes it to the visitors.)*

Visitor #1: Where is Sarah, your wife?

Abraham: She is in the tent.

Visitor #1: I was sent to tell you that she will have a son.

(Sarah peeks out of the tent and laughs loudly enough for all to hear.)

Visitor #2: Why does Sarah laugh? Is anything too hard for the Lord?

Sarah: *(Coming out of the tent.)* I did not laugh.

Visitor #3: Sarah, you did laugh.

Narrator: Sarah presses her hand to her heart and Abraham looks at her lovingly, because he can understand her fear. Now they realize that their three visitors were the Lord God, Jehovah, and two of His angels.

 SS1885

REBEKAH AT THE WELL

Based on Genesis 24
by Edith E. Cutting

CAST OF CHARACTERS

Narrator   Rebekah
Servant   Laban

Props: Water jar, bracelet and earrings

Scene: Bare stage

Narrator: Abraham did not want his son Isaac to marry a pagan woman from Canaan where they were living, but to have a wife from his own family who worshiped God. He sent his chief servant to find such a woman and make the arrangements.

The servant took ten camels and loaded them with costly presents to give to the family whose daughter he chose. Then he traveled several days till he came to the city of Nahor. There he had the camels kneel down outside the city, and he knelt down and prayed to God.

Servant: *(Enters and kneels.)* Oh, Lord, the women are coming to draw water from the well. Please give me a sign. When the girl you want my master's son to marry comes, let her give me a drink and offer, too, to draw water for my master's camels.

(Rebekah enters with her jar on her shoulder, crosses the stage, fills her jar offstage, and comes back.)

Servant: *(Stands.)* Please give me a drink of water from your jar.

Rebekah: *(Lowers jar.)* Drink, my lord. *(He drinks from jar.)* I will draw water for your camels, too. *(She goes offstage to draw water, brings it past the servant and out to his camels, crossing several times.)*

Servant: *(Takes bracelet and earrings from his girdle and gives them to her.)* Whose daughter are you? Is there room at your father's house for me to spend the night?

Rebekah: I am the daughter of Bethuel, and my family will welcome you. We have plenty of room as well as food for your camels. I will run and tell them a guest is coming. *(Leaves.)*

Servant: *(Kneels.)* Praise be to God, who has brought me to the house of my master's relatives and shown me the right woman to be the wife of my master's son.

Shining Star Publications, Copyright © 1991, A division of Good Apple

SS1885

Narrator:	Rebekah's brother came and welcomed Abraham's servant. Before the servant would eat, though, he told his story and the reason for his coming. He also gave the family beautiful gifts. The next morning he asked to leave, but Rebekah's mother and brother Laban wanted him to wait.
Laban:	Let my sister stay with us ten days, and you will be our guest.
Servant:	My master thanks you, but I must return to him quickly. He is eager to know that I have found a wife for his son.
Laban:	Let us call Rebekah and ask her. Rebekah! *(She enters.)* Will you go with this man?
Rebekah:	I will go.
Narrator:	So everyone hurried to get ready. Rebekah and her maids went with the servant to the home of Abraham and Sarah, and there she became Isaac's wife.

SS1885

JACOB AND RACHEL

Based on Genesis 29:1-14
by Helen Kitchell Evans

CAST OF CHARACTERS

Narrator   Rachel
Three men at well   Laban
Jacob

Narrator: Jacob went on a long journey. As he came into the land of the people of the East, he saw a well out in a field. Three flocks of sheep were lying near the well. He saw three men removing a large stone that covered the top of the well. They were getting ready to water their sheep. He walked over to them.

Jacob: Who are you men and where do you live?

1st man: We live in Haran.

Jacob: Do any of you know Laban, the son of Nahor?

2nd man: Yes, we all know him. He is a fine man.

Jacob: How is he? How is his health?

3rd man: As far as we know he is very good. We have not heard of any illness.

1st man: Here comes his daughter Rachel with her father's flock of sheep. *(Enter Rachel. She goes to the well.)*

Jacob: Let me help you. *(Goes to the well and lifts off the stone.)* Let me water your sheep for you. *(Kisses Rachel.)*

Rachel: *(Steps away from Jacob.)* Who are you? Why have you kissed me?

Jacob: Aren't you the daughter of Laban?

Rachel: Yes, but does that give you the right to kiss me?

Jacob: I am Jacob. My mother is Rebekah.

Rachel: Oh, I must tell my father you are here. *(Runs offstage, and returns with Laban, her father.)*

Laban: *(Embraces Jacob.)* My sister's son! Oh, how wonderful to see you. Come with us to our house. *(They leave.)*

Narrator: They talked about many things. They asked each other about other members of the family. They agreed that they were alike in many ways. Jacob stayed a month with Laban.

SS1885

JACOB'S VISION

Based on Genesis 28:10-22
by Helen Kitchell Evans

CAST OF CHARACTERS

Narrator
Jacob

Props: Rock, small bottle of "oil"

Narrator: Abraham's son, Isaac, was the father of Jacob. One night when Jacob was on a long journey, he slept on the ground. *(Enter Jacob tired from walking.)*

Jacob: My, I sure am tired! My feet are sore! It's sunset. I think I'll stop here and rest. I'll just put this stone under my head for a pillow. It's better than nothing. *(Picks up stone and settles down to sleep.)*

Narrator: Jacob begins to dream. He is restless all night. In the morning he awakens—startled. *(Jacob tosses and turns during this speech.)*

Jacob: *(Jumps to feet.)* My! It's daylight! I think I dreamed all night. There was this long ladder that went from earth to heaven. I saw angels going up and down. At the top of the ladder stood the Lord. I heard Him speak. *(Jacob sits down, holding his head in his hands.)*

Narrator: I am the Lord God of Abraham, your father. I am the God of Isaac. This land where you are I will give to you and to your children and grandchildren and all the people who will be born in the years to follow. I will take care of you. I will bring you back to this land.

Jacob: *(Stands.)* Am I awake now or still dreaming? *(Looks all around.)* Surely the Lord is in this place. I'm scared. This must be the gate of heaven. *(Lifts stone and moves it to another spot. Takes out a small bottle of oil and pours it over the stone.)* I shall call this place Bethel. Now, Lord, if you will be with me wherever I may go and will give me food and clothes, then will the Lord be my God forever. This stone shall be God's house. Of all that you give me I will give one-tenth to you. *(Jacob looks around again and leaves slowly.)*

JOSEPH'S COAT

Based on Genesis 37
by Marcia Hornok

CAST OF CHARACTERS

Narrator	Longer version: Simeon
Jacob	Gad
Joseph	Dan
	Three to seven brothers

Props: A long, colorful or ornate robe, wrapped in brown paper

Narrator: Long ago in the land of Israel lived a man named Jacob and his twelve sons. It's not right to have favorites, but Jacob did. He loved Joseph best. Did Joseph's older brothers like this? No, they didn't. It made them jealous of Joseph. Their father, Jacob, didn't make things any better. One day he gave a special gift to Joseph but not to the older brothers.

Jacob: *(Holding brown package.)* Joseph, my son, come see what I have for you.

Joseph: What is it, Father?

Jacob: Open and see.

Joseph: *(Opening package.)* Wow. It's a beautiful coat. Who's it for?

Jacob: *(Chuckling.)* It's for my best and brightest son, whom I love with all my heart.

Joseph: For me?

Jacob:	Yes, yes. Try it on. *(Helps Joseph with the coat.)*
Joseph:	*(Looking down at coat.)* It's beautiful. Oh, thank you, Father. I will wear it only on special days.
Jacob:	No, Joseph. I want you to wear this coat every day. You have outgrown your old one.
Joseph:	But Father, this coat will get in the way when I do my chores, and I'll dirty it taking care of the animals.
Jacob:	That's the point, my son. Your older brothers can do the dirty work. You don't have to. Just stay by me and keep me company. That will make me happy.
Joseph:	Thanks, Father. I'll take good care of my new coat. May I show it to everyone now?
Jacob:	Of course. Run along. *(Joseph exits.)*
Narrator:	As you might guess, Joseph's brothers were not happy to see his new coat. They knew it meant Joseph wouldn't be helping with the work. They began to look for ways to make things hard for Joseph. One day they did a very wicked thing. They sold Joseph as a slave, and he was taken to the country of Egypt.

(For shorter version, skip to Narrator's closing comments.)

(Scene opens with Simeon [holding Joseph's coat], Gad, Dan, and three to seven brothers standing with eyes shaded, looking toward the distance.)

Simeon:	There. That should take care of Joseph. He'll never bother us again.
Gad:	Maybe now Father will love us more.
Dan:	Yes. But what will we tell Father when Joseph doesn't come home?
Simeon:	*(Sits down, followed by brothers.)* I've already thought of that. We'll kill an animal and dip the coat in blood, then show it to Father. He can draw his own conclusions.
Dan:	Right! We'll say we haven't seen Joseph all day, but we found this bloody coat.
Gad:	Father will think Joseph has been killed by a wild animal.

(The brothers laugh at their cleverness as curtain falls.)

Narrator:	But God took the brothers' evil deed and turned it into something good. Over twenty years later, when Joseph was a ruler in Egypt, he saw his father and brothers again. He forgave his brothers, and they lived together as a family once more.

SS1885

JOSEPH'S SURPRISE

Based on Genesis 43-45
by Marcia Hornok

CAST OF CHARACTERS

Narrator	Judah
Joseph	Eight assorted brothers
Servant	Benjamin (smaller child)
Reuben	

Props: Silver cup, cloth handkerchief

Narrator: Over twenty years had passed since Joseph's brothers had sold him as a slave. They had nearly forgotten him, but Joseph was still alive in Egypt. He had some difficult times, but he kept trusting God and doing what was right. Eventually Joseph became a wise ruler over Egypt. He was in charge of selling food to all the countries that were having a famine. Even Joseph's brothers came to buy food from him. They did not know he was Joseph because he dressed and talked like an Egyptian. Joseph recognized them but decided to test them before letting them know he was their long-lost brother.

(Joseph is seated. Servant stands by him. The eleven brothers bow to him; then stand.)

Reuben: We have come to buy more food from you, your Honor.

Joseph: Where do you come from?

Judah: From the land of Canaan, your Honor.

Joseph:	*(Shouting.)* You are spies. You are here to see where our weak spots are so you can conquer us.
Reuben:	No, my Lord. There is no food left in Canaan. We came to Egypt only to buy food.
Joseph:	Very well. I will sell you food this time, but you had better not be lying to me. Now go. *(Brothers exit.)*
Joseph:	*(To servant.)* Sell those men grain, but put their money in their sacks when they're not looking. And put my silver cup in the youngest one's sack. *(Hands cup to servant.)*
Servant:	Yes, sir. It shall be done.
Narrator:	Joseph was testing his brothers to see if they would be mean to Benjamin as they had been to him years ago. After they started on their journey home, Joseph sent his guards to bring them back.

(Brothers fall to the ground in front of Joseph.)

Joseph:	Why have you stolen my silver cup? Your youngest brother who stole it will now stay here to be my slave.
Judah:	No, your honor. Do not take Benjamin. We will all be your slaves, but please let Benjamin go.
Reuben:	Yes, your honor. Our father will die if anything happens to Benjamin. Please take ME as your slave, not him.
Narrator:	Joseph saw that his brothers had passed the test. They were willing to give up their own lives for their youngest brother. He couldn't wait any longer to surprise them.
Joseph:	*(Shouting.)* Servants dismissed. *(Servant exits. Joseph buries head in his hands and cries into handkerchief. Wipes face and slowly looks at each brother before speaking.)* I am . . .Joseph. Is my father. . .still alive?

(Brothers stand up. . .look at Joseph and each other with puzzled looks.)

Joseph:	*(Extend hands to brothers.)* Come close to me. *(They do so.)* I am your brother Joseph— the one you sold as a slave. I'm not mad at you. God wanted me here in Egypt so I could sell you food during this famine.
Brothers:	*(Speak at once.)* It is Joseph. I can't believe it. This is amazing. Joseph, our brother?
Joseph:	Go quickly and tell my father I am still alive. Tell him God has made me a ruler in Egypt. Then bring him here to see me. *(Looks at Benjamin, goes to him, and they hug.)* Benjamin, my brother.
Narrator:	So Joseph's father and brothers and their families all moved to Goshen in Egypt, where Joseph took care of them. The family was finally together again.

SS1885

THE BABY IN THE BASKET

Based on Exodus 1:15-22, 2:1-10
by Marion Schoeberlein

CAST OF CHARACTERS

Miriam   Pharaoh's Daughter
Miriam's Mother   Narrator

Props: Doll in basket (symbolizing Moses)

Scene: Miriam and her mother bring the baby in the basket to the river.

Narrator: The children of Israel in Egypt had a new king. He was jealous of their power and strength and feared they might take over his throne. So he decided to kill all the Jewish boy babies who were born. This is the story of how one baby, called Moses, was saved.

Miriam's Mother: Oh, Miriam I am so afraid. Your little brother is so tiny he does not even have a name. Do you think he will be all right?

Miriam: Mother, we have prayed and prayed to Jehovah to protect him.

Miriam's Mother: I know, but I still can't help worrying.

Miriam: Mother, leave the baby here with me and go home. I will watch and see what happens. Someone is sure to find the basket.

Miriam's Mother: All right, but be very careful and stay here until someone finds him.

(Mother leaves the stage.)

(The basket is now at the far end of the stage and Miriam waits at the other end, standing behind some bushes. About two or three minutes elapse and then Pharaoh's daughter appears. She studies the basket. Then she picks it up.)

Pharaoh's daughter: This is a present sent by the gods. I have wanted a son for a long time and now I have one.

(Miriam walks slowly over to her.)

Miriam: My lady, shall I call you a nurse of the Hebrew women for the child?

Pharaoh's daughter: Go! Get a nurse at once! This day is blessed for me.

(Pharaoh's daughter walks offstage with the baby in the basket.)

Miriam: The Lord God of our fathers has answered our prayers. I cannot wait to tell my mother that she will be taking care of her own son. And in Pharaoh's palace, too! It is a miracle.

THE RED SEA

Based on Exodus 14:5-31
by Helen Kitchell Evans

CAST OF CHARACTERS

Narrator	1st follower
Pharaoh	2nd follower
Moses	3rd follower
	As many followers as desired

Props: Rod

Scene: Beside the Red Sea

Narrator: Pharaoh, King of Egypt, was told that the people of Israel had fled with Moses as their leader. The king was very angry.

Pharaoh: Why have we let Israel go? We need them to serve us! Get my chariot and 600 others. Get all the drivers. Call all the captains! Get everyone!

Narrator: So Pharaoh and all his chariots took off to follow the people of Israel. They found them camping beside the Red Sea. When the people saw the Egyptians they cried out in great fear.

1st follower: Have you taken all of us out here to die in this wilderness?

2nd follower: Why did you bring us out of Egypt?

3rd follower: Didn't we tell you that we wanted to stay and serve the Egyptians?

Moses: Yes, but we were all slaves!

1st follower: Who cares? That's better than dying in this wilderness!

Moses: Now don't be afraid. Keep quiet. You will see that the Lord will save us.

2nd follower: How? The Red Sea is on one side and the army of the Egyptians is on the other!

Moses: *(Looking up.)* Lord, Lord, save us!

Narrator: The Lord told Moses to speak to the children of Israel, to tell them to move forward toward the sea and have faith. He told Moses to lift the rod in his hand out over the sea. He told Moses that the Red Sea would divide and they would all pass across on dry land.

Then God caused a dark cloud to come over the Egyptians. They could not see the Israelites crossing. All were across safely when the cloud lifted. Pharaoh and his men followed. When all were in the sea, the Lord caused the water to move again. All the chariots and men were destroyed.

3rd follower: The Lord is with Moses!
The Lord is with us!
Lead on, Moses!

(All on stage march off following Moses. If desired, this playlet could be staged using elaborate costuming and many extra soldiers, etc., but may also be done simply and still give a great message.)

THE WALLS OF JERICHO

Based on Joshua 6:1-20
by Edith E. Cutting

CAST OF CHARACTERS

Narrator	Two Israelites
Joshua	Two angels (non-speaking parts)
Two priests	As many Israelites as possible

Scene: A circle of chairs, backs to outside, to represent the wall.

Narrator: Here within these walls is the great city of Jericho. The Israelites are sure God will help them take this mighty city, but they do not know how. Hear Joshua give instructions.

Joshua: Listen to me. This is what the Lord has told me. Tomorrow we shall all march silently around the city of Jericho.

1st priest: What good will that do unless the Lord goes with us?

Joshua: He will go with us. The ark of the Lord shall be carried before us.

2nd priest: People at the back cannot see the ark. How will they know that the Lord is with us?

Joshua: Seven priests shall blow on seven rams' horns, so that all people will know and march together.

1st Israelite: Will the walls of this great city fall just because we march around it once?

Joshua: No, indeed. You must wait and be constant in your faith.

2nd Israelite: For how long?

Joshua: For six days. One time each day, you shall march silently around this city. You shall not speak nor question the Lord in any way.

1st priest: Six days? But it is the seventh day that is holy to the Lord.

Joshua: That is true. On the seventh day we shall march around the whole city seven times, not just one time. We shall march in silence as before. Then when I say, "Shout!" you shall all shout at the tops of your voices.

Narrator: The first six days went by with nobody speaking while they marched once around the city each day. At last came the seventh day.

(All participants line up appropriately. One or more trumpet players blow steady march beats, offstage if necessary.)

Narrator: We now see the Israelites on their seventh and last time around the city of Jericho on that seventh day.

(All march around the city without speaking. At conclusion of circle. . .)

Joshua: Shout! For the Lord has given you the city.

All: Lord God! *(Angels rush in and push the wall so it comes crashing down, then leave.)* Praise be to God! *(Raise arms in exultation.)* Our Lord has given us the mighty city of Jericho.

SS1885

SAMSON AND DELILAH

Based on Judges 16:15-22
by Marion Schoeberlein

CAST OF CHARACTERS

Samson	Man who shaves Samson's hair
Delilah	Narrator

Props: Razor, wig

Scene: Samson lies on a couch, stroking his head. Delilah stands behind him, smiling craftily.

Narrator: Samson was one of the most important men in the Old Testament. He was so strong that he once killed a lion all by himself. Many were jealous of his strength, so his enemies sent a woman to trick Samson and find out the secret of his strength. Her name was Delilah, and Samson made a mistake when he fell in love with her.

Samson: Delilah, you are so beautiful. I've never loved a woman like you.

Delilah: I don't think you love me, Samson.

Samson: What makes you say that?

Delilah: Because you don't confide in me. You don't trust me.

Samson: I do trust you.

Delilah: Then why won't you tell me the source of your strength?

Samson: You've asked me that so many times. I'm tired of your trying to find out my secret, so I am going to tell you. It's because a razor has never touched my head.

Delilah: *(Laughing.)* Is that really true, Samson?

Samson: I swear that is the truth, woman.

Delilah: *(Giving Samson a hug.)* I'm so glad you finally told me. Now I know you love me.

Samson: Yes, I love you, but I'm very sleepy. I'm going to take a nap now.

Delilah: Yes, my love. Rest well, Samson.

(She leaves the room and Samson falls asleep. A few minutes later she comes back with one of her servants. He is carrying a razor. She points to Samson and whispers something into the servant's ear. The servant shaves off Samson's hair and it falls to the floor. Delilah laughs softly and leaves the room with her servant. Samson wakes up and sees his hair on the floor. He jumps up from his couch and reaches to touch his head.)

Samson: Lord God, my hair is gone! I feel very weak. The woman Delilah has tricked me! What a fool I have been!

 SS1885

RUTH

Based on Ruth 1-4
by Edith E. Cutting

CAST OF CHARACTERS

Narrator	Naomi
Ruth	Boaz
Orpah	

Scene: Bare stage

Narrator: In the land of Moab lived a man of Israel with his wife Naomi and two sons. The two sons married Moabite women, Ruth and Orpah. Years passed, and all three men died. Then Naomi decided to go back to Israel. Orpah and Ruth went with her to the boundary line. There Naomi said farewell to her daughters-in-law.

Naomi: Return now to your mother's house. May the Lord deal kindly with you as you dealt with my sons and me.

Orpah: *(Kisses Naomi on each cheek.)* Farewell to you. And blessings on you forever. *(Exits.)*

Naomi: Behold, Ruth. Orpah has gone back to her people and her gods. You should return also.

Ruth: Don't urge me to leave you or to turn back from you. Where you go I will go, and where you stay I will stay. Your people will be my people and your God, my God. *(Both leave stage but come back on as Narrator speaks.)*

Narrator: And so it was. Naomi and Ruth went on to Bethlehem. As days passed, Ruth gleaned in the fields to get grain for Naomi to use in making bread. One day she gleaned in the fields of Boaz, and he welcomed her kindly.

Ruth: *(Bowing deeply.)* Why have I found grace in your eyes? I am only a stranger.

Boaz: I have heard all that you have done for your mother-in-law. For her you left home and family. May a full reward be given you by the Lord God of Israel, under whose wings you have come for refuge. *(Both leave stage, then return at end of Narrator's speech.)*

Narrator: And so it was. Boaz watched over Ruth and gave her extra grain to take home to Naomi. After a time Boaz and Ruth were married.

Boaz: And our son was named Obed.

Narrator: In after years Obed named his son Jesse, and Jesse's son was David, the great King of Israel, the ancestor of Jesus, our Lord.

SS1885

HANNAH'S GIFT

Based on I Samuel 1:1-28
by Marion Schoeberlein

CAST OF CHARACTERS

Hannah	Elkanah
Two children	Peninnah
Samuel	Eli
Narrator	

Scene I

Setting: Elkanah and Hannah's tent. Hannah sits alone in front of Elkanah's tent.

Narrator: Hannah was a very important woman of the Old Testament. She wanted a child but couldn't have one. So her husband took another wife, Peninnah. This woman had many children and she treated Hannah cruelly. Peninnah thought she was a better person because she had given Elkanah a family.

(Peninnah enters smiling.)

Peninnah: Did you have a good time in Shiloh yesterday?

Hannah: Yes, Peninnah, I did!

Peninnah: *(Sarcastically.)* Don't tell me you are going to have a child!

Hannah: The secret of my happiness is mine to keep.

Peninnah: I saw you praying in the temple and talking to the priest. The other women thought you were drunk!

Hannah: Peninnah, I was not drunk!

Peninnah: Ha! I think you were!

Hannah: Peninnah, you have ridiculed me every time you could but now your days of ridicule are over!

Peninnah: I don't believe it! Even if you lie to Elkanah about having a child, he will always love me more than you! *(Peninnah leaves the stage shouting her last word.)*

(Two children come onstage and play in front of Hannah a few moments.)

Child #1: Our father, Elkanah, is coming.

(As Elkanah approaches, he pats them both on the head. Then the children leave the stage.)

Elkanah:	You're looking very happy today Hannah! You must have had a good time yesterday in the temple.
Hannah:	Do you love me, Elkanah?
Elkanah:	Of course I do. Is the same old thing bothering you? Not having a child! Don't you think I'm worth ten sons?
Hannah:	Elkanah, I have a secret to tell you.
Elkanah:	What is it, Hannah?
Hannah:	Yesterday I went into the temple to pray for a son. I met Eli, the high priest and at first he thought I was drunk. But then he heard the anguish of my heart in the prayer. He told me that God would answer my prayer and give me a child. You do believe me, don't you Elkanah?
Elkanah:	My dear wife, I do. If Eli, the priest said it, it will be!

(They both go into the tent and the curtain falls on first scene.)

Scene II

Setting: In the temple. We see Hannah giving Samuel as a gift to the Lord.

Narrator:	The Lord answered Hannah's prayer and gave her a son, whom she named Samuel.
Eli:	*(As Hannah and Samuel approach.)* Who have we here?
Hannah:	I am the woman who prayed for a child.
Eli:	Yes, now I remember you.
Hannah:	You told me the Lord of Israel would answer my prayer and He has. This is Samuel, the son I prayed for.

(Samuel bows to Eli.)

Eli:	He is a fine looking boy.
Hannah:	I bring him to you as a gift.
Eli:	A gift?
Hannah:	I promised the Lord that if He gave me a child I would dedicate him to the temple.
Eli:	You are a God-fearing woman and a thankful one.
Hannah:	I waited a long time for a son. Now I want to be worthy of that son. Samuel will serve you in the temple for the rest of his life.
Eli:	*(Turning to Samuel.)* Is this your wish, too, my son?

(Samuel nods his head and kneels down in front of the altar.)

Eli:	So be it!

DAVID ON THE ROAD

Based on I Samuel 17:1
by K. H. Munn

CAST OF CHARACTERS

Simon
David

Scene: Out in the country in ancient Israel, two boys dressed as shepherds are walking along a country road.

Simon: Awful thing, David, that our people are being attacked by that terrible strong army.

David: Yes, but the king heard about it and met them before they got to the city.

Simon: And they didn't even have time to gather food to take along.

David: My brother is going to be hungry. That's why Mother sent me with this food for him.

Simon: (Looking around with alarm.) Hope we don't meet any lions on the way.

David: (Swinging his sling.) Don't worry Simon. You've seen me use this on lions before. We'll be all right. Those things have hard heads but I've had to kill some to protect the flock.

Simon: Yes, you're pretty good with that thing.

David: Too bad you can't come all the way with me to the battlefield. I'd like to have you along.

Simon: The fork in the road where Mother told me to turn back to town is coming up. Guess I'll have to leave you here. Bye, David. (He turns back; they wave.)

SS1885

DAVID AND GOLIATH

Based on I Samuel 17:17-51
by Helen Kitchell Evans

CAST OF CHARACTERS

Narrator
Goliath
David

Props: Slingshot, five rocks, sword

Narrator: One morning David carried food into a camp where his brothers were serving in the army. While there, he heard about a terrible giant, an enemy of the men in his brother's army. All the Israelites were afraid because he was such a very, very big man.

Goliath: Send a man out to fight me!

David: I'll fight this giant!

Narrator: All the men in the army said that David could never win against this giant. David believed God would help him. So he went out to meet the giant. He carried only a sling shot and five rocks.

David: I can win!

Goliath: Who sends this child to fight me? Do you expect me to fight a child?

David: You have a sword, but come on and fight!

Narrator: So the giant raced toward David. David sent a rock toward the giant. It hit him in his forehead. David knew God would help him defeat the giant and his faith carried him through.

SS1885

FLYING CHARIOTS OF FIRE

Based on II Kings 2:11, 12
by K. H. Munn

CAST OF CHARACTERS

Joseph
Elisha

Scene: Two men talking. For staging they may be standing or sitting, either on rocks or chairs.

Joseph: Elisha, you are Elijah's disciple. Where is he?

Elisha: He's gone. I was walking along a road with him when suddenly a chariot of fire appeared and separated us.

Joseph: What did you do?

Elisha: I ran so that it would not hit me.

Joseph: Sounds frightening! Then what happened?

Elisha: After we were separated, I saw Elijah taken to heaven in a whirlwind.

Joseph: Anything else happen?

Elisha: Yes. After Elijah was taken up I cried, "My father! My father! The chariots and horsemen of Israel!" Then I saw him no more.

(Scene closes with dimmed lights, actors still in place.)

THE WISE KING

Based on I Kings 3:16-28
by Marion Schoeberlein

CAST OF CHARACTERS

King Solomon   Two Women
Servant   Narrator

Props: Doll, sword

Scene: King Solomon sits on a chair decorated like a throne. Two women coming in to see him are arguing. Second woman carries a baby.

Narrator: Long ago in biblical times there was a wise king. Some say he was the wisest man who ever lived. One day two women came to him with a story. They were fighting over a child. King Solomon had to find out who the real mother was because each one wanted the baby.

King Solomon: *(Motioning to arguing women.)* Enter.

(The two women enter, one carrying a doll symbolizing the child.)

First woman: Oh, great king *(she points to the woman carrying the baby)*, this woman stole my child!

King Solomon: How did she do that?

First woman: We both had babies at the same time, in the same house. Hers died in the night. Then while I was sleeping she came and stole my child!

Second woman: I did not steal her child! This baby is mine. She is lying! It was her child who died in the night!

King Solomon: *(Calling to servant standing at far end of stage.)* Bring me a sword.

(The servant brings him a sword.)

King Solomon: Bring the child to me!

(Second woman gives baby to the King.)

Second woman: What are you going to do?

King Solomon: Cut the baby in half. Then each one of you will have half of a child.

First woman: NO! NO! Oh great king give the child to her! I would rather have another woman raise my baby than have it die!

King Solomon: Now I know who the real mother is. *(Hands child to first woman.)* I will give her the child.

Narrator: The wise king knew that the real mother would not want her baby killed. By testing the two women he found out who the real mother was. This was only one of the wise things he did. God blessed King Solomon with wisdom and riches. He was said to be the wisest and richest king who ever lived!

SS1885

PLENTY TO SHARE

Based on I Kings 17:8-16
by Sandra Godfrey

CAST OF CHARACTERS

Narrator	Adriel
Mother	Elijah

Props: Food barrel

Scene I

Narrator: Adriel's stomach hurt as he bent to gather twigs from the dry ground. Crops had failed in the little village of Zarephath. For days Adriel and his mother had rationed the last of their water, meal, and oil. Inside their stone house they planned to light a fire, bake a cake of bread, and eat their last meal together.

Mother: *(Wearily.)* Come along, Adriel. We have enough wood for the fire.

Adriel: *(Wiping perspiration.)* Mother, why doesn't God do something? If He knows we are hungry, why doesn't He help us?

Narrator: In the afternoon sun Adriel saw the outline of an Israelite man coming toward them. His rough shirt was made of hair. His leather sandals were caked with dust from travel.

Elijah: *(Begging and breathless.)* Please! I'm thirsty. Give me a cup of water. *(Humbly, Adriel's mother bows her head and turns to go inside.)*

Adriel: *(In disbelief.)* Wait! Water? What does he mean asking us for water? We have nothing to share. We are about to starve.

Elijah: *(Calling to Adriel's mother.)* Please, help me. I need a cake of bread as well.

Adriel: *(Frustrated.)* Bread? Who is this man?

Mother: *(Looking humbly at Adriel and then at Elijah.)* I'm sorry, Sir, but we have no bread in the house. My son and I have just gathered a few sticks. We were going inside to cook our last meal.

Elijah:	*(Coming nearer, leaning on his staff.)* Don't be afraid. I am Elijah, prophet of the living God. In my heart I hear God whispering, "Share what you have. Then you will have plenty to drink until the rain falls and crops grow again."
Narrator:	From the look in his mother's eyes, Adriel knew what she planned to do. Hesitantly, he followed her inside.

Scene II

Elijah:	*(At the dinner table.)* Thank you, God, for this food you have provided. Bless it to our bodies, and bless these your servants. Amen.
Adriel:	*(Smelling the bread.)* Oh, Mother, this bread looks so good. But I'm. . .I'm worried. What will we do tomorrow, and the day after that?
Mother:	Adriel, we must trust completely in God.
Narrator:	When all the food was gone, Elijah and Adriel's mother continued talking. But Adriel could not keep his eyes off the empty meal barrel. Silently, he left the table. Standing on tiptoe he peered into the earthen jar.
Adriel:	*(Astonished.)* Mother! Mother! Come quick! It's true—just as Elijah said, just as God promised. We do have plenty to eat and plenty to share! *(Mother hurries to look in the barrel.)*
Narrator:	In that happy little home Adriel and his mother laughed together for the first time in many months. And, for the next two years, until the rains drenched the land, until crops grew in the fields again, the meal barrel at their house was never empty. Adriel knew that God loved his children, and was thankful!

QUEEN ESTHER

Based on Esther 2-7
by Edith E. Cutting

CAST OF CHARACTERS

Narrator	Esther
Mordecai	Hatach

Scene: Bare stage except for wall down the center dividing the queen's courtyard from the street. *(Hatach goes from one side to the other by an offstage door.)*

Narrator: In Persia during the reign of King Xerxes, a search was made for a beautiful girl to be his queen. Esther was the one he chose, and he set the royal crown on her head. Esther was an orphan Jewish girl who had been brought up by her older cousin, Mordecai. She was obedient to Mordecai's wishes and did not tell anyone that she was Jewish. A year or so after she became queen, a plot was made to kill all the Jews in the kingdom. Mordecai realized that only the queen could save them. Now was the time to tell everyone that she was Jewish. He could not go into the queen's courtyard, and Queen Esther could not come out to the street, so they sent word to each other through a messenger named Hatach.

SS1885

Mordecai:	*(Speaking to Hatach.)* Take my word to the queen. There is a terrible plot against all Jews. Ask her to go into the king's presence and plead with him for her people.
Hatach:	*(Bows, leaves, then appears in the courtyard, bowing before the queen. He repeats Mordecai's message.)* Mordecai sends word to you to ask the king. . . .
Esther:	Nobody can go before the king unless the king summons that person. If I should enter his court, I might be put to death. He could save me only by extending his golden scepter. Take this message to my cousin.

(Hatach leaves, then reappears in the street before Mordecai, and gives him Esther's message.)

Mordecai:	Tell the queen: When all Jews are condemned, do not think you will escape death just because you are in the king's house. If you do not speak for your people, God will help them in another way, but you and your father's family will perish. Who knows but that you were made queen for just such a time as this?

(Hatach takes the message to Esther.)

Esther:	Say to Mordecai: I will do your bidding. Now you must help me. Gather all Jews together and fast for three days. At the end of that time I will go to the king, even though it is against the law. And if I perish, I perish! *(She leaves the stage.)*

(Hatach takes the message to Mordecai.)

Narrator:	So Esther went to the king. She found favor in his sight and thus gained the right for Jews to defend themselves. All her people were saved by the courage of Queen Esther. She had offered her life for her people.

DANIEL MAKES A DECISION

Based on Daniel 1
by Marcia Hornok

CAST OF CHARACTERS

Daniel   Shadrach
Meshach   Abednego
King Nebuchadnezzar   Ashpenaz (the king's official)
Narrator

Narrator: Daniel, Shadrach, Meshach and Abednego were king's sons in Israel. But they were captured by the country of Babylon and taken to live there. Nebuchadnezzar, king of Babylon, became their new king.

King: *(Seated. Ashpenaz standing before him; D, S, M, A farther back.)* I want you to give these boys the best Babylonian education. They will live in the palace and eat my food and drink my wine for three years.

Ashpenaz: *(Bowing slightly.)* Yes, Your Majesty.

King: At the end of that time, I will test them and choose the best ones to work for me as my wise men.

Ashpenaz: Yes, Your Majesty. *(Bows. D, S, M, A bow and walk away. King and Ashpenaz walk away in other direction and exit.)*

Shadrach: Did you hear that? The king wants us in his service.

Meshach: Yes. We might become his wise men.

Abednego: I think we're going to like being captured.

SS1885

Daniel: Not so fast. Did you hear what we have to eat and drink?

Meshach: Yes. The king's meat and wine.

Shadrach: We can't drink wine. It's against God's law.

Abednego: And the king's meat includes things forbidden by Jewish law. Oh, what are we going to do?

Daniel: Well, I'm not going to eat it. I'll starve before I break God's law. Let's talk to Ashpenaz about it.

(Ashpenaz enters. Daniel speaks to him.)

Daniel: With all respect, sir, we cannot eat the king's meat or drink wine. It would defile us.

Ashpenaz: What can I do? If you don't look healthy and well-fed, the king will think I'm not doing my job and will put me to death.

Daniel: Please give us a test for ten days. Give me and my friends nothing but vegetables and water. The other students can eat the king's food. At the end of the ten days, you can see who's stronger.

Narrator: So Ashpenaz agreed to this. And God honored Daniel's decision. At the end of the test, Ashpenaz made a discovery.

Ashpenaz: It's amazing, Daniel. You and your three friends look healthier and are smarter than any of the young men who ate the king's food. From now on, everyone eats vegetables and water. *(Daniel and three friends cheer.)*

Narrator: Three years later, when their training was complete, King Nebuchadnezzar tested all the students.

King: The testing is finished. Ashpenaz, you have done a fine job. I commend you.

Ashpenaz: *(Bows slightly.)* Thank you, your Majesty.

King: I am pleased to announce that Daniel, Shadrach, Meshach and Abednego are ten times smarter than any of my wise men. They will be my personal advisors from now on.

Daniel: *(To the other three.)* God has given us these special abilities. We must keep obeying Him and putting Him first in all our decisions. *(All agree.)*

THREE YOUNG MEN

Based on Daniel 3
by Helen Kitchell Evans

CAST OF CHARACTERS

King Nebuchadnezzar   Shadrach
Meshach   Abednego
a Chaldean   Herald
Narrator

Props: Scroll, rope

Scene: King's Palace

(As the scene opens, the King is on his throne.)

Narrator: King Nebuchadnezzar had put up a golden statue and ordered everyone to worship this idol.

Herald: *(Enters with a scroll. He unrolls the proclamation and reads.)* You are commanded, O peoples, nations and all those of all languages, that when you hear the sound of the horn, pipe, bagpipe, or any kind of music, to fall down and worship the golden image that King Nebuchadnezzar has set up. Whoever does not fall down and worship it shall be put into a fiery furnace.

                      SS1885

Narrator: So all the people shouted, "O King, live forever!"

(Enter a Chaldean.)

Chaldean: O King, there are three men who refuse to worship the statue. They pay no heed to you. They will not serve your gods or worship this golden image which you have set up.

King: *(Jumps up in rage.)* Bring those men to me! I'll show them who is King!

(The Chaldean goes out and returns with three men. They stand before the King who is still standing.)

King: Is it true that you three refuse to worship the golden image? Is it true you refuse to serve my gods? When you hear music will you bow down? If not, into the fiery furnace you go. You'll see. Whose God do you think will protect you?

Shadrach: We have no need to answer you.

Meshach: Our God whom we serve is able to deliver us from the fiery furnace.

Abednego: We will not serve your gods or worship this golden image.

King: *(Shaking fists.)* Heat the furnace seven times hotter than usual. Tie up these men, throw them into the furnace.

(The Chaldean throws a rope around them and leads them away. King goes to side of stage to watch where the men are led. There is a long pause.)

King: Look! Didn't we throw them into the fire? Look in there!

Herald: I see four men loose, walking in the the fire. They are not hurt.

King: That is what I saw. Who is that fourth figure? *(King steps forward and calls out.)* Shadrach, Meschach, and Abednego, come out of there! *(The three young men walk out onstage. King touches their heads. Even the hair had not been singed. They look the same. Their clothes have not burned. Kings throws up his hands.)* O blessed be the God of Shadrach, Meshach, and Abednego! Their God sent an angel to deliver them. I saw the angel in the furnace! I now make a decree: Any people or nation that speaks a word against the God of these men shall be torn limb by limb, their houses laid in ruins, for there is no other god who is able to do anything like this. We shall worship the God of Shadrach, Meshach and Abednego! Forever! Forever!

DANIEL DISOBEYS THE KING

Based on Daniel 6
by Marcia Hornok

CAST OF CHARACTERS

Daniel   Governor
King Darius   Officer
Narrator

Governor: *(To officer.)* Did you hear the latest? It's not enough that King Darius made Daniel a president. Now he wants to put him in charge of the whole country.

Officer: I know. It's disgusting. Hey, maybe if we watch Daniel closely, he'll make a mistake and we can tell the king.

Governor: Are you kidding? Daniel never does anything wrong. He's always honest and right, and he even prays three times a day.

Officer: Hey. That's it! We'll get the king to make a law Daniel has to break.

Governor: What do you mean?

Officer: Come on, I'll show you. *(They go to the king.)* King Darius, live forever. I wish that everyone felt about you the way we do.

King: What do you mean?

Officer: You are so wise and powerful. You're almost like a. . .well, a god. I wish we had a law that no one could make requests to anyone but you for a whole month.

Governor: Yes. For 30 days let no one pray to anyone except you. Whoever breaks the law will be thrown to the lions.

King: You flatter me. But I see your point. You write the new law, and I'll sign it. *(All exit.)*

SS1885

Daniel:	*(Kneels and looks up.)* Jehovah God, I seek You now. I will continue to pray to you even though it's against the king's law. Please help me be brave enough to bear the punishment.
Officer:	*(Enters.)* Look, there's Daniel praying to his God instead of the king. *(Shouting.)* Guards! Arrest that man. *(All exit.)*

(King sits, Officer and Governor approach with Daniel between them.)

Governor:	Oh King, live forever. We both are witnesses that this man, Daniel, has broken your new law about praying.
King:	Oh no, I didn't mean that Daniel couldn't pray to his God.
Officer:	Isn't it true, King Darius, that any law you sign cannot be changed?
King:	Why, yes, but you have trapped me. Daniel, I'm so sorry I had no idea what these men were up to when I signed that silly law. *(Sigh.)* Perhaps your God will rescue you.

(Governor and Officer roughly pull Daniel offstage.)

Narrator:	So Daniel was thrown to the lions. But the king stayed up all night, worrying about Daniel.
King:	*(Pacing back and forth across stage.)* I never should have let those men trick me into signing that law. Now I've lost my wisest and best man. Oh, what'll I do?
Narrator:	Early the next morning, the king hurried to the lion's den to see what had become of Daniel.
King:	*(Cupping hands to mouth.)* Daniel, servant of the Most High God. Was your God able to deliver you?
Daniel's voice offstage:	King Darius, live forever. God has sent His angel to shut the lions' mouths because I have done nothing wrong.
King:	Glory be to God. Guards! Bring Daniel out at once. Now throw the Governor and Officer to the lions. *(Pause.)* Hmmmm. Looks like the lions are hungry after all.
	Now I make a new law that cannot be changed. Everyone in my kingdom must worship the God of Daniel, for He is the only true and living God.

SS1885

JONAH

Based on Jonah 2:10-3:2
by K. H. Munn

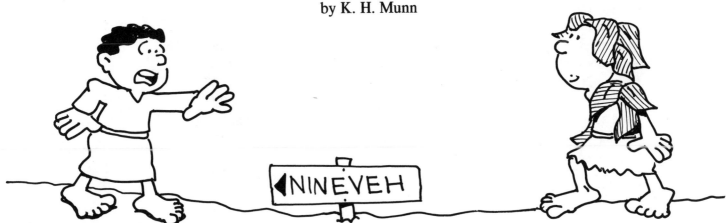

CAST OF CHARACTERS

Jonah
Boy
Simon

Scene: Boy is sitting on a beach. Sign in the background says "Nineveh," with arrow pointing toward where it might be. A raggedy "monster" comes staggering down the beach—rags (to simulate seaweed) partially wrapped around his head and upper body—that's why he appears to be a monster. Boy (dressed in "Israelite" robes) attempts to hide, but the "monster" sees him.

Jonah: Hello, boy. It's great to be on land! Isn't it?

Boy: *(Shouting.)* Go away sea monster!

Jonah: *(Unwrapping "seaweed.")* Ugh, this seaweed does get in the way!

Boy: *(Feeling better.)* Mister, you sure do smell like fish!

Jonah: Yes, those fish can be trouble when they try to digest you.

Simon: *(Walking up to Jonah and boy.)* What are you doing here on the beach?

Jonah: God wanted me to go to Nineveh and warn them about their sinful ways. I didn't want to and I tried to hide.

Simon: Did you get in trouble?

Jonah: I got tossed off a ship by the sailors and I ended up in the belly of a fish.

Simon: If God wants you to warn Nineveh. You'd better go.

Jonah: Yes, it's big trouble when you disobey God! Which way to the city?

(Simon points towards the sign, Jonah looks at it and walks off toward Nineveh. Jonah waves to Simon.)

SS1885

OLD TESTAMENT INDEX

NEW TESTAMENT SKITS

Shining Star Publications, Copyright © 1991, A division of Good Apple
SS1885

IT'S COMING

Based on Luke 19:44, 21:8-13
by K. H. Munn

CAST OF CHARACTERS

Peter
Jesus
A group of people

Scene: Jesus, Peter and a group of people stand outside a great, beautiful temple.

Peter: The temple is so beautiful!

Jesus: As for what you see here, the time will come when none of these stones will be left on another. Every one of them will be thrown down.

Peter: Teacher, when will these things happen? How will we know that it's time for it to happen?

Jesus: Watch out that no one fools you. Many will say, "I am he," and, "The time is near." Do not follow them. When you hear of wars and bad people don't be afraid. These things have to happen first, but it will be a while until the end. Look at the trees. When they sprout leaves you know summer is coming. When you see lots of earthquakes and famines, you will know about that, too. It won't be long then.

(Peter looks frightened.)

Jesus: Don't worry, I'll be with you.

THE BRIDEGROOM PARABLE

Based on Matthew 25:1-13
by K. H. Munn

CAST OF CHARACTERS

Rebecca   Two groups of girls
Deborah   Offstage voice

Scene: Two groups of girls, holding lamps, Rebecca in one and Deborah in the other, standing expectantly.

Rebecca: The bridegroom told us to wait for him and it's getting dark. Sure am glad that I filled my lamp.

Deborah: Filled your lamp? I forgot to.

Several other girls in the group: Yes, me too.

Girls standing near Rebecca: My lamp is full. I'm ready.

Rebecca: *(Pointing offstage.)* Hooray, here comes the bridegroom!

Girls without oil for their lamps: Oh, no! We don't have any oil! Give us some of yours.

Rebecca and "ready" girls: No, you can't have any of ours. We must be ready to greet the bridegroom. Go buy some oil.

Unprepared girls: *(Walking off stage dejectedly.)* We didn't get ourselves ready!

Loud voice offstage: Be ready for your bridegroom, fill your lamps, prepare yourselves. Jesus will come for His church!

SS1885

ROAD TO JERUSALEM

Based on Luke 19:29-34
by K. H. Munn

CAST OF CHARACTERS

Disciple 1   Jesus
Disciple 2   Group of Israelites

Scene: Jesus and Disciple 1 approach a town through the city gate. Disciple 1 is wearing a sword. A group of Israelites walk a short distance behind. Disciple 2 is in the group.

Disciple 1:   I don't like this, Lord. People here want to kill you.

Jesus: That's the story of my life. I was sent to this place by my Father to meet those people. It is necessary. You and everyone to come needs for me to be here at this time.

Disciple 1:   Well, at least we will arrive in time for the Passover meal. Maybe those people will be so busy with that they won't think of you.

Jesus: Yes. And we'll have our own Passover meal in Jerusalem before I am betrayed to them. It has to be done.

Disciple 1:   I don't want them to kill you, Lord. That's why I'm wearing this sword. *(Pats the sword.)* It's nice and sharp. I'll protect you. You will be safe in the city.

Jesus: Maybe, but first, I need a very young donkey to ride into town, just a colt. Go to that village just ahead.

Disciple 1:   Where will I find a donkey colt?

Jesus: As you enter the village you will find a colt tied there that no one has ever ridden. Untie it and bring it to me.

Disciple 1:   *(Motioning toward the group of people walking behind them.)* Come on. We're going to get a donkey colt for Jesus to ride. *(Disciple 2 comes running up and they start to run ahead to the town.)*

Jesus: If anyone asks you why you are untying it, tell them that the Lord needs it.

Disciple 1:   Yes, Lord. *(Disciple 1 and Disciple 2 run off ahead.)*

Scene closes with the lights being slowly dimmed to darkness, actors still in place on the stage.

SS1885

PERFUME FOR JESUS

Based on Matthew 26:6-13
by Marion Schoeberlein

CAST OF CHARACTERS

Jesus	Woman
His disciples	Narrator

Scene: Simon's house in Bethany. A table with two chairs and with a woman seated in one of them. A bottle of perfume is on the table. Jesus comes in with His disciples and sits down at the far end of the table. The disciples gather around the woman.

Narrator: One of the most beautiful stories of the New Testament is the story of the woman who poured perfume on Jesus' head. He was very impressed with her gift.

Jesus: This is a good resting place. Simon's house is always good to visit.

(The disciples nod. The woman studies Jesus carefully; then she gets up and takes the bottle of perfume over to the place where Jesus is sitting. Carefully she pours it over His head. The disciples gasp and grumble amoung themselves. The woman smiles. Jesus smiles back at her.)

Disciple: Master, this is expensive perfume she has wasted on you. It was a foolish act. The money she spent for the perfume could have been given to the poor.

(Jesus shakes his head.)

Jesus: You are wrong. She has done a beautiful thing. Remember, the poor will always be with you. But I will not always be with you. This woman poured perfume on My head in honor of My burial. Believe me, this woman's act will be remembered. Some day the world will honor her for the act she has performed.

(Woman walks away and disciples look ashamed.)

SS1885

A NIGHT IN BETHLEHEM

Based on Luke 2:1-7
by Helen Kitchell Evans

CAST OF CHARACTERS

Joshua
David

Scene: Two boys are talking.

Joshua: *(Points.)* Who are those people?

David: *(Turning head.)* Where? Oh, you mean that man leading a donkey? With the woman riding the donkey?

Joshua: Yes, have you ever seen them around here before? The woman looks so tired.

David: Well, it isn't easy to ride a long time on a donkey. I'd rather walk.

Joshua: But look! She's too heavy to walk very far!

David: I noticed. She looks like my mother did when she was heavy with my little brother. She looks like she might have that baby any time.

Joshua: I sure hope she makes it into Bethlehem.

David: My hope is that they can find a place to stay. It is crowded in Bethlehem. I understand every place where people stay is full. Dad said the inn was full yesterday.

Joshua: It's all because of Caesar Augustus.

David: I know. He's making every one in the world go back to their hometowns to pay taxes.

Joshua: My dad said that he was glad we lived in Bethlehem and didn't have to travel here to find a place to stay.

David: Joshua, something keeps going through my mind.

Joshua: What? No telling what could be going through your mind. *(Laughs.)*

David: No, seriously. There's a story going around town that a Messiah will soon be born. Wouldn't it be neat if this woman's child turned out to the Messiah? Better still, that he would be born in our town of Bethlehem?

Joshua: Come on, David. We better head for home. What a mind!

David: But just think what we could tell our children. We would have seen a prophecy being fulfilled.

Joshua: Well, come on. I suppose we will know before long. News gets around pretty fast in Bethlehem.

David: No one would ever forget that kind of news.

(These last two speeches are given as the boys move slowly offstage.)

SS1885

THE FIRST MIRACLE

Based on John 2:1-11
by Marion Schoeberlein

CAST OF CHARACTERS

Narrator	Jesus
Jesus' disciples	Mary, Jesus' Mother
Two servants	Bride and bridegroom
Small group	

Scene I

Setting: A garden where six water jugs are standing.

Narrator: It was at the wedding at Cana that Jesus performed His first miracle. We can be sure He was as happy as the bride and bridegroom because He gave them a gift they would always remember—the miracle of wine made out of water.

First Servant: *(To Second Servant)* Look, the jugs of wine are empty. *(Mary is standing nearby and overhears the conversation.)*

Second Servant: What shall we tell the bridegroom? A wedding is not a wedding without wine.

First Servant: We should have planned this wedding better. But we did not know so many people would come. We should have made more wine. Now the guests will leave early and the bridegroom will blame us.

Mary: I couldn't help hearing your problem with the wine.

First Servant: Do you have a suggestion?

Mary: Yes, my son Jesus is coming. He will soon be here with His disciples. He will help you.

Second Servant: *(Coming over to them.)* Who is this son of yours? What can he do that we cannot do?

Mary: You will see. Jesus is a special person. He will know what to do, I am sure. Look, He is coming now.

First Servant: Well, if he can perform miracles, Woman, he is the man for us. Otherwise, we will just be wasting time telling him about our problem. It is too late to make new wine now.

(Jesus comes and greets His Mother. The disciples stand behind Him.)

Mary: Jesus, they have no more wine at the wedding today.

Jesus: *(Sounding very authorative.)* Woman, what have I to do with you? My hour is not yet come. *(He walks off a little way to where the bride and bridegroom are standing, a circle of people around them.)*

Mary: *(To the two servants.)* Whatever He tells you to do, do it.

First Servant: I don't know if what she says is true, but it won't hurt us to keep standing here. It's better than telling the bride and bridegroom what a predicament we are in.

Scene II

Narrator: There was dancing at weddings in biblical times. It signified the great joy and happiness of the day. As this scene opens, the bride and bridegroom are dancing for the crowd around them.

(Jesus comes over to the water jugs to join the two servants.)

Jesus: Fill the waterpots with water. Then bring them back here to me.

(Servants, grumbling, pick up the jugs and take them out. They bring the water jugs back and put them down at Jesus' feet.)

Jesus: Now taste the wine before you take it back to the bridegroom.

(The servants dip out a little water.)

First Servant: I don't believe it. This is the best wine I ever tasted. Much better than the first wine we had.

Second Servant: *(Shaking his head.)* You're right. This man is a miracle worker. We must take this wine to the bridegroom right away. The crowd has been asking for it.

(Jesus and His disciples walk off the stage. Servants carry two jugs to the bridegroom.)

First Servant: Look, Master, here is the new wine.

Bridegroom: *(Tasting it.)* This is delicious. *(He hands some to his bride.)* In fact, I have never tasted any wine like it. Usually the best wine is served first at a wedding, but you two have saved the best until last. You are to be congratulated!

(Servants walk away from bride and bridegroom and crowd moves back to the other water jugs.)

First Servant: That woman who spoke to us has a Son who knows a mystery we do not know. Shall we tell the bridegroom about Him?

Second Servant: No, I think we should keep our secret. This man will become famous soon enough if He goes to all the weddings here in Cana and turns water into wine.

First Servant: Yes. We will not be able to keep our secret long. Just for today, let the bridegroom think it was our doing.

(Curtain closes as they leave the stage smiling. The bride and bridegroom do another little dance as the crowd claps their hands.)

THE TEMPTATION

Based on Matthew 4:1-11
by Marion Schoeberlein

CAST OF CHARACTERS

| Jesus | Angel |
| Satan | Narrator |

Props: Two stones

Scene: A desert scene. . .Jesus walks in the sand alone for a few moments. Then Satan (dressed like an old man in a black cloak) enters. In the background is a pinnacle where Jesus stands as Satan enters.

Narrator: Jesus was in the desert fasting and thinking. He saw no one except the wild animals there. Because he hadn't eaten anything for forty days, He was very hungry. Satan thought this was a good time to come to Him. This is the story of Jesus' temptation.

(Satan moves stealthily toward Jesus, two stones in his hands.)

Satan: You've been wandering out here a long time. You must be very hungry by now. Here, I have two stones. They say You are the Son of God. Well, if You really are, why don't You make these into bread?

Jesus: It is written in the Scripture, man shall not live by bread alone, but by every Word of God.

(Jesus walks to the center of the stage where the pinnacle is and puts His feet on it. Satan comes up behind Him, laughing softly.)

Satan: If You really are the Son of God, cast Yourself down from here. You have plenty of angels. They will keep You from falling.

Jesus: Do not tempt me, Satan!

Satan: I know something better. Look down from this pinnacle and see all the glories of this world. I have them all—the kingdoms of this earth. Everything down there belongs to me. If You will fall down and worship me, I will give them all to You.

Jesus: Get behind me, Satan. It is written, you shall worship only the Lord, Your God.

(Satan leaves stage muttering. Angel comes and stands on pinnacle above Jesus and touches Him on the shoulder.)

FISHERS OF MEN

Based on Luke 5:1-11
by Helen Kitchell Evans

CAST OF CHARACTERS

Simon	Jacob
Pete	Narrator

Narrator: As Jesus was walking by the Sea of Galilee, he saw Simon and Andrew casting a net into the sea. These men made their living by fishing. A little farther down along the lake Jesus saw James and John, the sons of Zebedee. These brothers were mending their nets.

As usual there were people following Jesus. Among those that day were two children named Pete and Jacob. As the scene opens, these friends are talking.

Pete: Why do crowds follow Jesus everywhere he goes?

Jacob: I suppose because they are curious, like us, to see Jesus.

Pete: Look over there right now. Jesus is getting into Simon's boat. Listen, what's he saying? *(Pause.)*

Jacob: He told Simon to move the boat out a little farther from shore.

Pete: I wonder what for.

Jacob:	Look! He's standing up in the boat. Jesus is going to speak to the crowd from the boat.
Narrator:	The people sat quietly and listened to Jesus. When he had finished, he told Simon to move his boat out farther into the sea and then let down his nets.
Simon:	*(Coming onstage.)* Master, we have fished all night and have caught nothing. What's the use? *(Pause)* Oh, well, what do we have to lose? *(Turns and goes offstage.)*
Narrator:	The net filled with so many fish that it broke under the load. *(Simon comes onstage and calls.)*
Simon:	James, John, come help us load all this fish. We're going to sink under the heavy load. *(Stays onstage.)*
Narrator:	James and John helped Simon and Andrew, then Simon fell on his knees at the feet of Jesus.
Simon:	*(Falling on his knees and looking up.)* Leave me, Jesus, I am a sinful man. You were the one who placed all those fish in the sea, then guided us to them.
Narrator:	Then Jesus reached out his hand and said. "Fear not, you shall catch men instead of fish. You will help me tell the story of my Father in Heaven." *(Simon slowly rises, then turns and walks as though following Jesus across stage and off.)*
Jacob:	Isn't that something? Those men just left their nets and followed Jesus.
Pete:	I wonder how they will make a living?
Jacob:	If Jesus could place all those fish in the sea in one spot for them to catch, He will provide for them.
Pete:	I guess you are right. We must have faith in what Jesus says. Not only us, but all the people who will live on this earth.
Jacob:	Do you think Jesus will live forever on this earth?
Pete:	Who knows? We may see many things happen in our lifetime. We'd better go back home.
Jacob:	You're right. Let's go. *(They leave.)*

(This playlet could have scenes showing all four of the fishermen in pantomime, but the theme may be sucessfully developed without using any of the characters spoken of by the narrator, except Simon. All that is happening is seen through the conversation of the two young boys, Pete and Jacob.)

A PARALYTIC MAN

Based on Mark 2:1-12
by Helen Kitchell Evans

CAST OF CHARACTERS

Esther
Naomi
Ruth

Scene: Capernaum

(As the scene opens, the three children are talking. They stand a short distance from a crowd of people around a house where Jesus has stayed overnight.)

Ruth: We'll just stand here and see what's happening.

Esther: Are you sure Jesus is in that house?

Naomi: Oh, I think Ruth is right. My folks said this morning that Jesus spent the night there.

Ruth: He's been drawing crowds every place he goes. He's been healing people who are sick.

SS1885

Esther:	Are you sure they are healed?
Ruth:	That's what everyone says. Many have seen their friends healed.
Naomi:	Here's your chance. See those four men carrying a man who can't walk?
Esther:	Oh! That's my neighbor! He's been ill for years.
Naomi:	Isn't that the person who shakes all the time?
Ruth:	You are right. It's awful! Look! Look! The crowd is so large the men can't get to the door of the house.
Esther:	They're climbing up on the roof with that sick man!
Naomi:	They are tearing a hole in the roof! Imagine that! *(Pause.)*
Esther:	Let's move in a little closer. *(They do so.)*
Ruth:	Now they are letting the man down through the hole in the roof. They are trying to get to Jesus.
Naomi:	Let's move still closer so we can hear what is being said. *(They move forward again onstage.)*
Esther:	That man close to the door said that Jesus had forgiven the man's sins.
Ruth:	How could Jesus do that?
Naomi:	That's what the scribe just asked.
Ruth:	Only God can forgive sins.
Naomi:	That's what the scribe just said.
Esther:	Sh! There's Jesus at the door. He said that the Son of God has power to heal on this earth.
Naomi:	Look! Look! Look! Your neighbor is walking!
Esther:	I'm scared.
Ruth:	Why?
Esther:	I've never seen anything like this before, that's why! Who is this Jesus?
Naomi:	His followers say He is the Son of God sent to earth.
Esther:	You mean He's the one we hear about who was born in Bethlehem long before we were born?
Naomi:	The very same one.
Esther:	Let's hurry to my house. I want to talk to my neighbor when he gets home.

THE LOST SHEEP

Based on Luke 15:3-7
by Marion Schoeberlein

CAST OF CHARACTERS

Jesus, the Good Shepherd   Boy passing by
Man passing by   The Lost Sheep
A group of sheep   Narrator

Scene: A grassy, hilly scene. The lost sheep is standing with other sheep. He wanders to the far end of the stage. After a few minutes the other sheep leave the stage and the lost sheep stands there all alone.

Narrator: Jesus told many stories to teach a lesson. This story of the lost sheep is one of the most beautiful He ever told and is about all of us.

Lost Sheep: It's such a pretty day. I'll just run by myself a little while and find a good spot to graze.

Boy passing by: Hello, sheep. Are you all alone? You must be lost. I wish you were mine. Then I could take you home.

(Boy leaves the stage.)

Lost Sheep: This is fun, but now I'm getting tired of being alone. I wish I was with the other sheep. Being with them and the shepherd makes me feel safe.

Man passing by: This is a strange sight. One sheep all alone. Someone will come along and steal him. It's a good thing I'm an honest man or I would steal him myself.

(Man leaves the stage.)

Lost Sheep: I feel so alone. What will happen to me? A wolf might come and eat me. I wish I hadn't wandered away from the others. If only the shepherd would come and find me. *(Sheep hangs his head. Jesus, the Good Shepherd, comes on stage. Pats the sheep on the head.)*

Jesus: Here you are, my lost sheep! I'm so happy to find you. It's a good thing I went out looking or you might have been stolen or killed. Come on, little sheep, you'll be safe now. You're with me. I'll always protect you.

(The Lost Sheep and Jesus, the Good Shepherd, leave the stage.)

Shining Star Publications, Copyright © 1991, A division of Good Apple

SS1885

PRODIGAL SON

Based on Luke 15:11-32
by Helen Kitchell Evans

CAST OF CHARACTERS

Narrator	Young son
Older son	Farmer
Servant	Father

Props: Robe, ring, shoes

Scene: The young son comes home.

Narrator: There was a man who had two sons. We now hear the young son talking to his father.

Young son: Father, why don't you give me now what I would inherit?

Father: Why now?

Young son: Well, I want to get out and see the world. I want to enjoy life while I am young.

Father: I suppose I could, but I hope you will use the money wisely.

Young son: Oh sure! I'll do that! *(They leave stage.)*

Narrator: A few days later, the young man took off for a far away country. He wasted all his money going to parties and having a great time spending money on friends. He never thought of trying to find a job. He spent all he had. There came a time upon this land when there was great famine. The young man was hungry. He went out looking for work.

(Enter a farmer and young man.)

SS1885

Young son:	I am glad I met you. I am down on my luck. Could you give me a job?
Farmer:	Well, I could use some help feeding my pigs. Not much of a job, but better than nothing. Come along. *(They leave stage.)*
Narrator:	The young man was so hungry he ate the husks from the corn he fed the pigs. He stood in the pig lot talking to himself. Listen.
Young son:	*(Enters.)* Look at the kind servants my father has. They have all they can eat and some left to spare. Here I stand among these pigs starving. I'm going home. *(Leaves.)*
Narrator:	So the young man traveled home, staggering with hunger. He saw his father running to meet him, a servant following. *(The father and son embrace.)*
Young son:	Father, I am a sinner. I am not worthy to be your son. Let me be your hired servant. I am starving.
Father:	I'll hear no more of this. Come here. *(Motions to servant.)* Go get my best robe, my ring and shoes. Then get a fat calf and prepare it for a feast. This, my son, is alive! He was lost! Now he is home! Let's celebrate! *(Servant leaves, returns with items. Son puts on robe, etc.)*
Narrator:	They had music and dancing. The older son came to the house to see what was happening. *(Enter older son.)*
Older son:	Why this celebration? No one told me about it.
Father:	See, your brother has returned. We are celebrating his return.
Older son:	Well, I've stayed home and worked hard for you. I haven't seen any great celebration for me.
Father:	Son, you have always been with me. All I have is yours, but this is your brother who was lost! He is alive! He was lost and now is found! Come join us!

(Father and young son go offstage, then slowly the older son walks off, head down.)

ZACCHAEUS IN THE SYCAMORE TREE

Based on Luke 19:1-10
by Helen Kitchell Evans

CAST OF CHARACTERS

Zacchaeus
A friend
Narrator

Scene: Jericho

Narrator: One day Jesus came to Jericho. In this town lived Zacchaeus, a very rich man, chief of the tax collectors. He had heard about Jesus. When he heard that Jesus was in town, he followed the crowd around him. But Zacchaeus was a very short man and he couldn't see Jesus in the crowd. Now we see Zacchaeus and a friend.

Zacchaeus: How am I going to see Jesus in this crowd? I'm too short. I'm getting squeezed flat in here.

Friend: Well, it's a shame you are so short. There's a sycamore tree not far away. Climb it!

Zacchaeus: Great idea! I'll do just that. *(A cardboard tree could be placed in front of a step ladder, or character could pantomime climbing a tree.)*

Narrator: So there was Zacchaeus, high in a tree. As Jesus came by, Zacchaeus had a great view. Also the crowd had a great view of Zacchaeus. Jesus saw him and told him to come down out of the tree and to hurry because he planned to stay in his house.

Zacchaeus: *(Turning to friend.)* I'm so pleased to have Jesus stay with me in my house.

Friend: I'm surprised. Lots of people think you are a sinner.

Zacchaeus: I'm going to change. Half of what I own I am going to give to the poor. If I have taken money from some that I shouldn't, I will pay them back four times as much.

Narrator: Jesus said, "Today salvation has come to the house of Zacchaeus. The Son of Man has come to seek and to save that which was lost." Jesus led the way and Zacchaeus and his friend followed. *(They all leave the stage.)*

SS1885

HEALING THE BENT WOMAN

Based on Luke 13:10-17
by Helen Kitchell Evans

CAST OF CHARACTERS

Jesus	Woman
Ruler	Crowd
Narrator	

Scene: The crowd is seated as though listening to a speaker.

Narrator: Jesus was teaching in one of the synagogues on the Sabbath. Among the people listening was a little woman who was so bent that she could not stand up straight. For 18 years she had walked bent over so far that she looked only at the ground. When Jesus saw her he called to her and healed her.

Jesus: "Woman, you are now able to stand up straight." *(Jesus laid his hands upon her and she faced the crowd, who saw that she had been healed.)*

Woman: Praise be to God! Praise the Lord Jesus! Look! I can walk straight. *(She walks around stage.)* I can face forward like all of you! I can walk straight because of Jesus!

Ruler: *(Stands up.)* There are six days in a week to heal people. We don't work here on the Sabbath. The Sabbath is a day of rest. It is a holy day. People who want to be healed should come other days, not on the Sabbath.

(Woman starts to leave, stops when she hears Jesus speaking.)

Jesus: "You hypocrites! Don't you untie your ox or donkey from the manger and lead it to get water to drink on the Sabbath? Shouldn't this woman, bent for 18 years, be healed even on the Sabbath?"

Ruler: Yes, Master, we are ashamed of how we have behaved this day. Let us all rejoice that the woman has been healed! Glorious things have been done today!

Crowd: Glory be to God! Bless Jesus, the Son of God! *(The healed woman leaves followed by the crowd.)*

Ruler: *(Leaves.)* Praise be to the Lord!

DOUBTING THOMAS

Based on John 20:24-29
by Marion Schoeberlein

CAST OF CHARACTERS

Jesus   Thomas
Ten disciples   Narrator

Scene: A room where the disciples are gathered. They are talking about seeing Jesus.

Narrator: The disciples were very sad after Jesus' death, but they had faith. They knew they would see Him again, and when He appeared to them, they were overjoyed. One of them, Thomas, was not with them when Jesus showed Himself to the disciples after His resurrection.

     This is the story of that doubting disciple and how he found faith again.

(Disciples are sitting around the table talking and eating as the scene opens.)

Disciple 1:   I keep wondering if the Lord will come to us again.

Disciple 2:   That would be wonderful.

 SS1885

Disciple 1:   I keep remembering His message, "As my Father hath sent Me, even so send I you."

Disciple 3:   He gave us the Holy Spirit, too, and the power to forgive sins—think of it!

Thomas: *(Rises angrily from the table.)* I've thought about it a lot and I don't believe any of you. I think you're all making up the story to make yourselves feel good. Or maybe you all had too much to drink!

Disciple 1:   I tell you, we all saw Him, Thomas. You weren't here. Maybe you're just jealous because we saw the Lord, and you didn't.

Thomas: I'm not jealous. Just realistic!

Disciple 2:   You always were the doubter among us, Thomas, just the way Judas was the money-lover.

Thomas: I tell you that unless I see the print of the nails in His feet and hands and put my hand into His side I will not believe it! *(Thomas goes to the door, and stands there.)*

(Slowly Jesus, in a white robe, walks through the open door.)

Jesus: Peace be unto you.

(The disciples crowd around him, all but Thomas, who is too shocked to move. Jesus beckons for Thomas to come near, and Thomas slowly walks forward to Jesus.)

Jesus: Thomas, look at my hands and my feet that still have the print of the nails in them. Put your hand into My side, too. Do not doubt Me, but believe.

(Thomas puts his hand into Jesus' side and then falls to his knees.)

Thomas: My Lord and my God!

Jesus: Because you have seen Me, Thomas, you believe. Blessed are all those who have not seen and still have believed!

ANANIAS

Based on Acts 9
by Marion Schoeberlein

CAST OF CHARACTERS

Narrator
God's Voice
Ananias

Scene: Ananias' house

Narrator: The story of Saul's conversion is one we can never forget. He was the man who persecuted the Christians until one day he met Christ on the road to Damascus. He was struck with blindness and his friends had to lead him home.

But after he got home the Lord sent a very important man into his life. That man's name was Ananias. He gave Saul's eyesight back to him and was his first real Christian friend.

This is the story of how God came to Ananias in a vision.

(Ananias is lying on his bed sleeping.)

God's Voice: *(Calls name two or three times.)* Ananias!

Ananias: *(Wakes slowly, sits up.)* I'm here, Lord.

God's Voice: Get up and go to the house of Judas on a street called Straight. A man called Saul of Tarsus is staying there. He is praying because he is blind. I gave him a vision of you, Ananias. He is waiting for you to come and give him back his eyesight.

Ananias: Lord, I can't go there! I've heard a lot about this man. He has done nothing but evil to your followers. He will persecute me, too. In Jerusalem he has authority from the chief priests to bind everyone who calls on your name.

God's Voice: Don't be afraid, but go your way. Saul of Tarsus is a chosen vessel. He will speak My Name before the Gentiles and even kings. He will speak My Name before the children of Israel.

I will show him what great things he must suffer for My Name's sake.

(Ananias gets out of bed and kneels down to pray.)

Ananias: Lord, help me.

(Ananias gets up and, as he leaves the stage, the Voice of God is heard in the distance.)

God's Voice: I will help you, Ananias.

SS1885

SIMON AND THE HOLY SPIRIT

Based on Acts 8:17-25
by Marion Schoeberlein

CAST OF CHARACTERS

Simon	Benitus (Simon's friend)
Peter	John
Philip	Eight to ten people receiving the Holy Spirit
Narrator	

Props: Bag of coins

Scene: A hilly spot in Samaria where people are receiving the Holy Spirit by the laying on of hands.

Narrator: After Jesus' death, the disciples continued preaching His Word and healing in His Name. Philip baptized many people in Samaria and his work was so successful that Peter and John went to that city to help him.

Simon, a magician who practiced sorcery there, heard about their miracles and wanted the same power of healing they had. He wanted it so badly that he was willing to pay a lot of money for it.

This story is about what happened to Simon when he asked Peter for the Holy Spirit.

(Peter, John and Philip are standing at the far end of the stage laying their hands on the people, saying very softly, "Receive ye the Holy Spirit." Simon and his friend enter at the other end of the stage. Simon is carrying a bag of silver that jingles.)

 SS1885

Simon:	I came prepared, Benitus. Every man has his price and I'll pay a lot of money to the man who gives me the power of that Holy Spirit.
Benitus:	I'm not surprised you're so generous! You used to be popular here with your sorcery, but when these disciples of Jesus came, the people turned to them.
Simon:	Who is that big rugged man? He looks like the important one to me.
Benitus:	I heard his name is Peter.
Simon:	Good. I'm going up to him and ask for the Holy Spirit.
Benitus:	Just like that? You have a lot of nerve.
Simon:	Come on, Benitus. Let's go.

(As Simon and Benitus approach Peter, the crowd that received the Holy Spirit leaves the stage.)

Simon:	*(Jingling his bag of coins and facing Peter.)* I have heard of your many miracles. I will pay you a handsome sum of money for your power.
Peter:	*(Angrily.)* Do you think you can buy the gift of the Holy Spirit? God does not sell it for money!
Simon:	*(Falling to his knees.)* Please! I will pay any price!
Peter:	I don't want your money! Believe me, your heart and your motives are all wrong!
Simon:	Tell me what I must do!
Peter:	You must repent of your wickedness. You must ask God's forgiveness. If you do not, He will punish you!
Simon:	Pray to the Lord for me, I beg you, that He may forgive me!

(Simon rises and sighs loudly. Then he turns to his friend and they walk away. Before he leaves the stage Simon flings the bag of coins away.)

Narrator:	Peter and John prayed for Simon before they returned to Jerusalem.

LYDIA

Based on Acts 16:14-16
by Marion Schoeberlein

CAST OF CHARACTERS

Lydia   Claudia
People passing by   Narrator

Scene: A street scene in Philippi. Lydia and her friend, Claudia, are selling their purple garments.

Narrator: A woman by the name of Lydia was Paul and Silas' first convert in Europe.

              Not too much is written about this woman except that she was a seller of purple-dyed garments and that she and her family were converted and baptized by Paul.

              This is the story of how she showed her thanks to Paul.

Lydia: The crowds are good today, Claudia. We will sell a lot of cloth.

Claudia: I think there are so many people in the town because Paul and Silas have come here. Everyone is being baptized—or haven't you heard?

Lydia: You may be surprised, Claudia, but I've been baptized by them myself! They preach the true God.

Claudia: I am surprised! What about your family?

Lydia: They have been converted and were baptized, too. How do you feel about Paul and Silas?

Claudia: I have to have some more time to think about their preaching.

Lydia: I have asked Paul and Silas to come and stay with me a while. When they come, I want you to come, too, and listen to them again.

Claudia: Maybe it would help me to make up my mind. Tell me, Lydia, why did you invite them?

Lydia: I am thankful to God for converting me through them. I need to hear more about the Gospel of Salvation and so does my household.

Claudia: Do you think they will come?

Lydia: Paul and Silas are men of God, Claudia. They keep their word.

Claudia: Then I will come, too. I've heard them preaching to a crowd. Now I'm anxious to meet them in your house.

NEW TESTAMENT INDEX

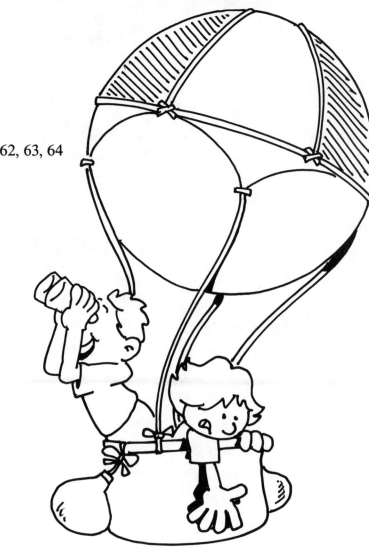

BIBLE SONGS

THANK YOU, GOD!

Words and Music by
Helen Friesen

SS1885

YOUTHFUL DAVID

**Words and Music by
Helen Friesen**

1. Da - vid, the son of Jes - se, lived in his home near Beth - le - hem.
2. Da - vid was called a hand - some lad; God told the pro - phet, "He's the one."
3. King Saul was trou - bled, plain to see. "Who will do bat - tle with this man?"

Sam - u - el looked at those sev - en sons, but God said it was none of them.
Sam - uel a - noint - ed God's choice for king; then he went home, for the deed was done.
If he succeeds I'll re - ward him well." Da - vid stepped forth, "I will fight this man."

"Have you no oth - er sons but these?" "Yes," an - swered Jes - se, "there is one,
"Da - vid," said Jes - se, "take this food. Go find your bro - thers with King Saul."
Pick - ing his way to the stream be - low, He found five stones that pleased him well.

He tends the flocks of sheep I own." "Send for him now, I must see that son."
When Da - vid reached the ar - my camp, he saw a man near - ly ten feet tall.
Armed with his sling - shot Da - vid went; my how the might - y gi - ant fell.

SS1885

JOSEPH, SON OF JACOB

Words and Music by
Helen Friesen

O COME, LET US SING

Words Based on Psalm 95:1,2
Music by Vickie Garrison

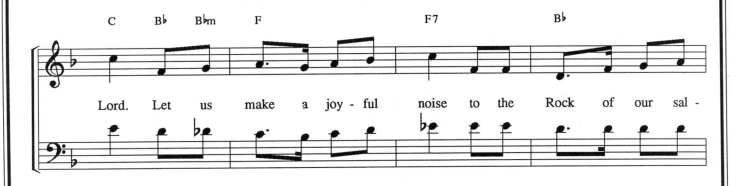

SS1885

SING UNTO GOD

Words Based on Psalm 68:32
Music by Helen Friesen

Sing un-to God, ye king-doms of the earth; Sing un-to God, ye king-doms of the earth; O sing prais - es, O sing prais - es, Sing un-to God, ye king-doms of earth; O sing prais-es un-to the Lord; Se - lah.

SS1885

MAKE A JOYFUL NOISE

Words Based on Psalm 100
Music by Helen Friesen

SS1885

THE LORD'S PRAYER

Words Based on Matthew 6:9-13
Music by Helen Friesen

SS1885

SS1885

TAKE UP YOUR CROSS

Words Based on Matthew 16:24-27
Music by Helen Friesen

If an-y one would come af-ter me, he must de-ny him-self and take up his cross and fol-low me. For who ev-er wants to save his life will lose it, but who-ev-er los-es his life for me will find it.

SS1885

GREATEST IN THE KINGDOM

Words Based on Matthew 18:2-5
Music by Helen Friesen

He called a lit-tle child___ and had him stand___ a-mong them. And He___ said:___ "I tell you the truth,___ un-less you___ change and be-come like lit-tle child-ren, you will___ nev-er en-ter the king-dom of heaven. Therefore, who-ev-er hum-bles him-self like___ this___

SS1885

SS1885

I WILL BE WITH YOU ALWAYS

Words Based on Matthew 28:18-20
Music By Helen Friesen

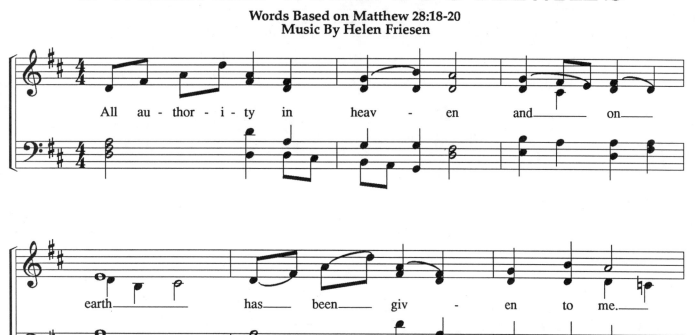

All au-thor-i-ty in heav-en and on

earth has been giv-en to me.

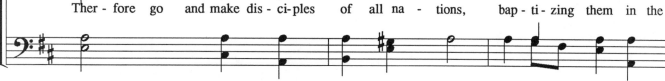

Ther-fore go and make dis-ci-ples of all na-tions, bap-ti-zing them in the

name of the Fa-ther and of the Son and of the Ho-ly Spir-it, and

SS1885

SUFFER THE LITTLE CHILDREN

Words Based on Mark 10:14-16
Music by Helen Friesen

Suf-fer the lit-tle child-ren to come, to come un-to me, and for-

bid them not, for-bid them not; for of such is the king-dom of God.

Ver-i-ly I say un-to you, Who-so-ev-er shall not re-ceive the

king-dom of God as a lit-tle child, he shall not en-ter there-

in. And he took them up in His arms, put his

hands up-on them, and blessed them.

LOVE THE LORD YOUR GOD

Words based on Mark 12:30-31
Music by Helen Friesen

SS1885

FIVE LOAVES, TWO FISHES

Words based on John 6:5-14
Music by Margaret McKinney Baker

One, two, three, four, five loaves, two fish - es, one, two, three, four, five loaves, two fish - es;

One, two, three, four, five loaves, two fish - es to feed five thou - sand hun - gry men. *FINE*

1. Je - sus sat high up - on the mountain top, and He— preached to five thou-sand men. He
2. Here's a lad with five loaves, two fish - es; That's not e - nough for five thou-sand men. But
3. Je - sus said "Go gath - er what's left_____ to make— sure that noth - ing is lost. They
4. Nev - er doubt the pow - er of Je - sus. If you're— hun - gry, He'll feed you too.

D.C. al Fine

preached so long_____ He had to— feed— them. How will He feed five_____ thou - sand men?
Je - sus gave— thanks and told his dis - ci - ples, "Go feed the five thou-sand hun - gry men."
filled twelve bas - kets with crumbs from the bar-ley loaves, Af - ter they fed five_____ thou - sand men.
Not with bar - ley loaves and two small— fish - es, But with the Word from the mouth of God.

SS1885

NO GREATER JOY

Words Based on III John 4
Music by Helen Friesen

I have no great-er joy than to hear that my child-ren walk in truth. I have no great-er joy than to hear my child-ren walk in truth; no great-er joy no great-er joy, I have no great-er joy; I have no great-er joy than to hear my child-ren walk in truth.

SS1885

A NEW COMMANDMENT

Words based on John 13:34-35
Music by Helen Friesen

91

SS1885

CREATIVE COSTUMING IDEAS

by Gail K. Beard

BASE COSTUMES:

Use light- or medium-weight polyester material so it can be cut without raveling (no need to hem.) Measure the child from shoulder to ankle (or knee for short costume.) For width, have child stretch out arms and measure from one wrist to the other. Fold yardage so edges meet and cut out neck and arm holes as illustrated. Sew inside-out from bottom edge to underarm and out to the edge of the sleeve. (Old sheets can be used, however, they must be hemmed in order to be reusable.)

FOR A SLEEVELESS BASE COSTUME:

Cut neck; then sew inside out from bottom edge on each side to within 4″ to 6″ from shoulder (depending on size of actors).

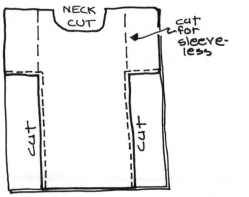

FOR WOMEN:

Use white or cream-colored polyester for the base costume. Complete costumes with polyester strips (18″ x 36″) of assorted colors (blue, orange, green, yellow) to wrap around head and body (see illustration).

FOR MEN:

Use off-white or beige for shepherd, official, and soldier base costume; brown, gray or black for others. Complete outfit with long vest (shown below) made in contrasting or complementary colors (rust, gold, green, brown, black) and matching headdress.

FOR KING:

Make base costume out of rich, deep-colored purple or gold. (Optional: Make a matching or contrasting vest.) Add lots of jewelry and metallic-colored braid for a belt. Add headdress and/or crown.

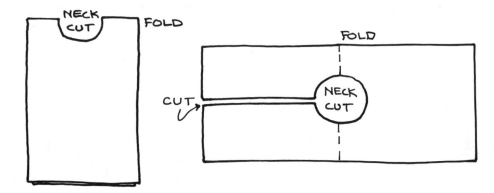

VEST:

With fabric folded so edges meet, cut neck opening. Cut center front open from neckline to bottom edge. Sew sideseams with right sides together to within 4″ to 6″ of the shoulder.

SS1885

ACCESSORIES

SOLDIERS' ARMOR:

Brush on thinned glue and sprinkle with gold or silver glitter or spray paint silver or gold. Decorate with sequins or metallic braid. (If using armor for Goliath, make each piece much larger than the regular soldier's size.) Soldier should wear short base outfit (and/or shorts) under the armor.

HELMET:

Use a small box and follow illustration to cut opening for face. Spray paint gold or silver.

BODY ARMOR:

Using large box, cut off bottom and cut out neck and arm holes. Box should be long enough to reach above the child's knees. Spray paint gold or silver.

SHIN GUARDS:

Using illustration as a guide, cut shin guards out of heavy tagboard. Add glitter or spray paint. Glue on gold- or silver-covered elastic leaving each end 5″ long to tie around back of legs.

SHIELD:

Cut large circle (approximately 12″ in diameter, depending on size of children in skit) out of tagboard. Use glitter or paint as suggested. Decorate with pretty rocks, metallic rickrack, or sequins. Glue a 1″ x 4″ piece of vinyl to back for handle.

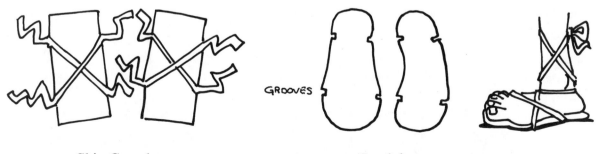

Shin Guards   Sandals

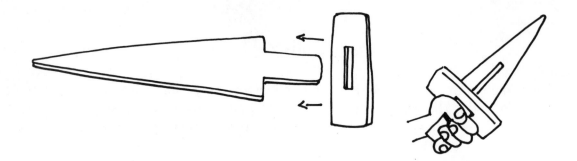

SWORD:
From illustrated example, cut a sword out of heavy tagboard. Use one color of glitter or paint for blade and a different color of glitter or paint for handle.

SANDALS:
Cut shoe shape out of heavy brown vinyl upholstery material. Attach 44″ strings in place on sides of vinyl as shown to allow strings to be criss-crossed under sandal heel, across ankle, up lower leg, and tied behind knee. (See illustration.)

KING'S CROWN:
Enlarge pattern and trace on heavy tagboard. Cut out, brush on thinned glue and sprinkle with gold or silver glitter (or spray paint gold or silver). Decorate with sequins, fake jewels, or metallic braid. Attach Velcro strips to allow it to be worn on different-sized heads. (Optional: For differently shaped crown, cut as above except cut zigzags [ᐱᐱᐱᐱᐱ] across the center top.)

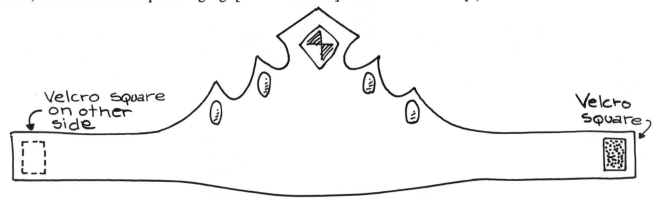

DAVID'S SLINGSHOT:
Find a sturdy forked branch and cut to size desired. Cut an oversized rubber band in half and tie an end to each fork. Use small, dark-colored, foam-rubber balls as rocks.

BEARDS AND SAMSON'S WIG:
Use dark-brown or black fake fur. Attach narrow elastic to corners to allow it to be tied behind the head or under chin.

BELTS:
Use twine or plain or metallic braid, depending on character being portrayed.

HEADDRESSES:
Cut polyester material (18″ x 24″) from coordinating or contrasting colors. (Use rich, brightly colored scarves for kings and place crown on top.) Tie on head with plain or metallic braid, depending on character being portrayed.

SS1885

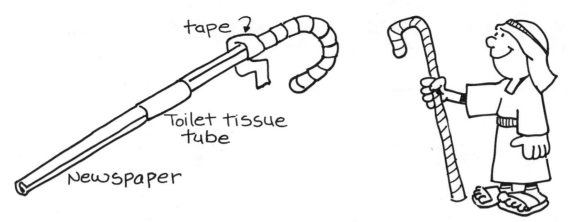

DAVID'S CROOK:

Roll two sheets of newspaper lengthwise. Secure both rolls with tape at either end. Place one end of both rolls of newspaper inside a toilet tissue tube and wrap with masking tape to create one long paper roll. Shape one end of roll to form the crook. Wrap with masking tape and cover with brown or green crepe paper.

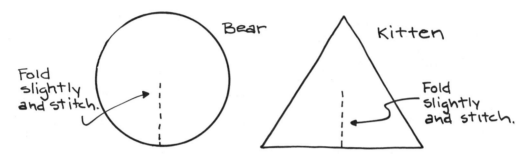

BEARS AND KITTENS:

Use brown base costumes for the bears and yellow base costumes for the kittens. Felt scraps can be used for ears. Following patterns, make round, brown ears for bears and pointed, yellow ears for the kittens; glue ears onto headbands. With eyeliner pencil, draw whiskers. Dot nose with red lipstick.

EGYPTIAN'S COSTUME:

Use a man's round-necked T-shirt for a tunic (size depends on child's size.) Using shiny gold material, make a wide belt, wrist and ankle cuffs, a wide gold collar, and a headdress (see illustrations). Gold sandals would complete the outfit.

AWARD CERTIFICATES

BIBLE PERFORMANCE AWARD

TO: _____

FOR: _____

_____
signature

_____
date

BIBLE PERFORMANCE AWARD

TO: _____

FOR: _____

_____
signature

_____
date

SS1885